Introduction

We hope you enjoy our interpretations of the lives and times of some of our most famous saints. Much of what we have discovered finds its origins in myth and legend. However, monks like St Bede, who wrote detailed accounts of many of the saints lives, together with ancient texts, has helped us to bring further light on the difficult journey to introduce Christian faith, in Great Britain and throughout the world.

Colour, keep and learn as you work your way through this unique activity book.

Contents

Written and illustrated by Les Ives
With thanks to the Rev. Ron Dale
for his help and support
Published by Colour History Ltd © 2005

St Andrew c. 60 AD
Patron Saint of Scotland
Feast Day 30th November

Andrew was believed to have been born in Galilee and spent the early part of his life as a fisherman. When Andrew met Jesus he was already a disciple of John the Baptist. Andrew introduced his brother, Simon Peter, to Jesus and they both became his disciples, listening to his teachings as often as they could. Eventually Jesus asked them both to leave their fishing nets behind and follow Him, to become "fishers of men".

One day a large crowd of five thousand people had followed Jesus to listen to him preach. They had wandered far away from their towns and villages, the day was hot and the crowd grew increasingly tired and hungry. Andrew pointed to a young boy in the crowd who was carrying five loaves of bread and two fishes. Jesus broke the bread and divided the fishes, miraculously feeding 5,000 people from the small basket of food.

Andrew was one of the first four apostles and one of the original Christian missionaries to spread Christianity throughout Asia and Greece. The Romans were fearful of the new faith and arrested him. He is believed to have been crucified in southern Greece. He took many days to die in the heat of the sun, but his faith was so strong that he preached to the watching crowd until he died.

For over 300 years Andrew's bones lay in a tomb until a Greek monk called St Rule, dreamt that Andrew's body should be removed. He took a tooth, arm bone, kneecap and finger bones as instructed in his dream, and set off on his journey to transport them to the "ends of the earth."

He set sail in a small boat and was eventually ship-wrecked on the wild east coast of Scotland. The local tribesmen, the Pict's, were fascinated by the stranger from far away and allowed him to stay. St Rule converted many of the local people to Christianity and they built a chapel to house St Andrew's remains. This is said to be the site of St Andrew's Cathedral today.

Did You Know?
The famous cross of St Andrew represents the cross shaped crucifix on which Andrew died. It is now the flag of Scotland.

St Rule lands in Scotland
with the bones of St Andrew

St George c. 303AD
Patron Saint of England
Feast day 23rd April

It is believed that George was born to Christian parents in an ancient land we now know as Turkey. George was a knight admired for his physical strength and bravery in battle. Great wealth and power could have been his, but a wave of hostility towards Christians angered George and he decided to declare his own faith. He tore down notices warning of further persecutions and he was arrested.

During his captivity he endured terrible beatings with clubs, was boiled in molten lead, clasped in red-hot irons, forced to drink deadly poison and tied to revolving spiked wheels to crush him to death. Amazingly his faith restored him to health each time, but eventually it was ordered that he was to be beheaded. As George lay dead bolts of fire were sent from Heaven, destroying the buildings and idols of the heathen priests who had witnessed his suffering.

Stories of his faith and bravery spread across the world and he became the patron saint of many countries. In England his name was adopted by King Richard I, who greatly admired George and he called upon his name to protect the crusader armies. Later Henry V made a famous speech before the battle of Agincourt, declaring St George the Patron Saint of England.

The legend of George and the dragon is ancient. Apparently the ferocious beast, with foul breath had been terrorising a local kingdom, and each day two sheep were offered to keep the dragon satisfied. Once the sheep had run out, human victims were required. The king's own daughter drew the first lot and was to become the beast's next sacrifice. Dressed as a bride the young girl was taken to the dragon's lair and left to meet her fate. George arrived just in time, wounding the beast with his lance. The princess's corset was used to make a lead to walk the beast into town as if it were tame! George made the king promise that he and his subjects would live according to Christian values, and only then did George slay the troublesome beast.

> ***Did You Know?***
> *It is said that King Richard I had a vision in which he saw George bearing a mighty banner with a red cross on it. The cross was adopted to protect and give courage to his knights.*

Brave St George fights with
the ferocious dragon

St Patrick c. 389 - 461 AD
Patron Saint of Ireland
Feast Day 17th March

Patrick was born in England of Christian parents, but at the age of sixteen his village was raided by pirates from Ireland. He was bundled onto the pirate's ship and spent the next six years looking after cows and pigs in a hostile land far away from home. One night in a restless sleep Patrick had a dream that a voice whispered "Lo, thy ship is ready". Rising from his sleep the young man escaped to the coast where he persuaded the sailors of a waiting ship to accept him on board. After facing near starvation he impressed the captain and crew by praying for food, saving them all from certain death. After many adventures Patrick finally returned home to his family, but he was a changed man.

Some time later a second voice spoke to him instructing him to return to Ireland to spread the word of Christianity. Patrick prepared for his task, spending time in a French monastery. Fifteen years later he was ordained by Pope Celestine and he returned to Ireland, where he faced great danger from the Druids who lived there.

One myth tells us that it was traditional to extinguish all village camp fires and only the king was allowed to re-light them, to celebrate the return of the sun. However, Patrick's fire burned brightly to celebrate the resurrection of Christ. King Laoghaire was furious and he demanded to see the person who had dared to defy the sacred tradition. Patrick was brought before the king and his warriors, but they were impressed by the way Patrick spoke and his deep faith. He was allowed to stay and preached to the king and his subjects.

In 444AD Patrick founded the cathedral church of Armagh and soon it became a centre for education and administration. Christianity spread throughout Ireland and gradually the old Druid rituals disappeared. The Irish symbol of the shamrock is said to originate from Patrick, who on plucking one from the ground described the three leaves as representing the Father, the Son and the Holy Spirit. The place of his death and burial are not known.

> **Did You Know?**
> *Whilst out walking with his magic staff,*
> *Patrick was confronted by a horde of*
> *vicious snakes. Waving his staff he*
> *banished the snakes from his sight*
> *and Ireland.*

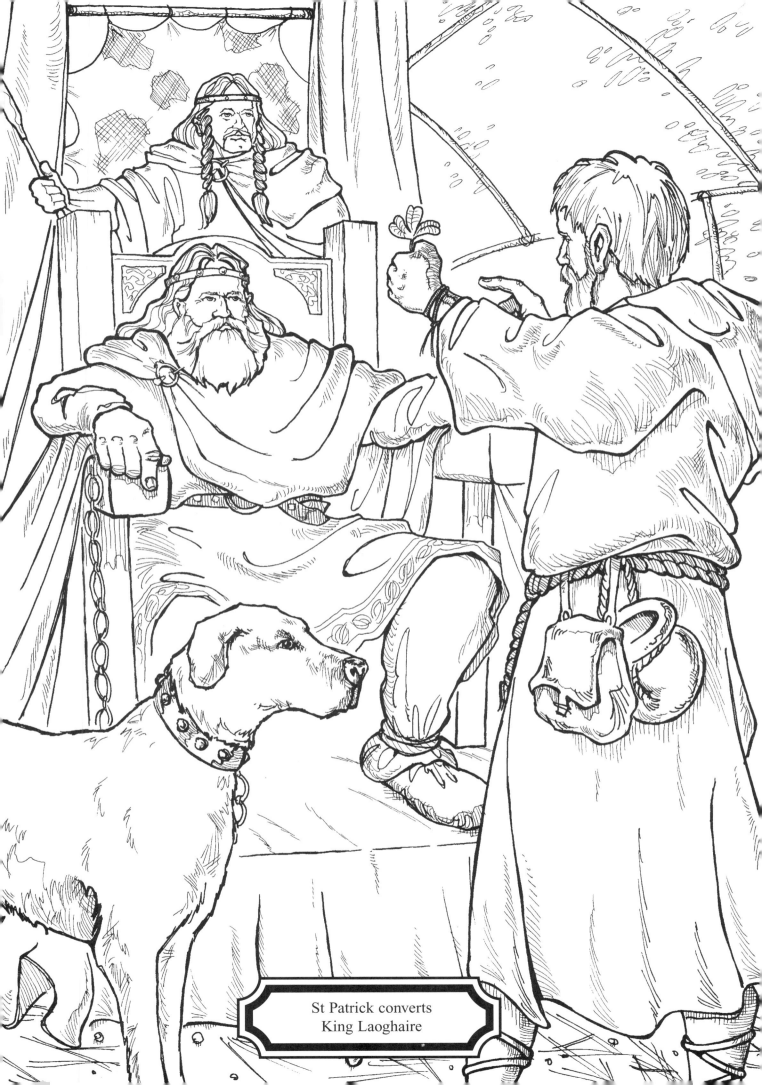

St Patrick converts
King Laoghaire

St David (Dewi) c. 520 - 589AD?
Patron Saint of Wales
Feast Day 1st March

David was the son of a prince, but turned his back on his comfortable beginnings, studying the psalms and eventually becoming a priest. He established 12 monasteries and churches, firstly Glastonbury and then Bath, where he is said to have blessed the deadly water making it heated and healing. After many years of travelling he settled at Menevia, or Mynyw with his disciples.

Life was very harsh here with many hours spent in silent prayer and many more in the fields. The use of oxen and ploughs was not permitted and the monks lived on bread and vegetables. Although he was kind and generous David did not allow the consumption of anything other than water, and he became known as "The Waterman".

David was summoned to the synod at Cardigan and when asked to speak his voice was said to have rung out as clear as a silver trumpet. He was unanimously elected primate of the Cambrian church. When he took his place on the throne, a white dove was said to have settled on his shoulder. He died a very old man and his last words were said to be "Be joyful, brothers and sisters. Keep your faith, and do the little things that you have seen and heard with me."

St Winifred (St Gwenfrewi) c. 650 AD
Feast Day 3rd November

Winifred's mother was the sister of St Beuno and she was delighted when her uncle settled nearby. She eagerly listened to his teachings, which deeply affected her. As she grew older the beautiful Winifred attracted the unwelcome attentions of Caradog, the son of a local chieftain. Her repeated refusals to accept his love sent Caradog into a rage and he chased her, as she ran for the shelter of her uncle's newly built church. At the door of the church he struck her with a vicious blow, cutting off the young girl's head with his sword.

Caradog was immediately swallowed-up by the earth and the place where Winifred's head lay became a beautiful fresh water spring. The pebbles and rocks at the bottom of the stream were streaked with red, like the stains of Winifred's blood. St Beuno began to pray and Winifred was raised from the dead, her head joined to her body, showing only a scar. Holywell, or Tre Ffynnon is said to be the site of the miraculous stream.

Winifred's faith was even stronger now and she worked tirelessly, becoming the abbess of Gwytherin in Denbighshire. Fifteen years after her miraculous resurrection she died. She was the Patron Saint of Wales until her remains, which were enshrined at Gwytherin, were taken to Shrewsbury Abbey in 1138.

Did you know?
The tradition of wearing a leek is said to have come from an ancient battle when soldiers were asked to wear one in their caps, to help recognise each other in the heat of battle.

St Winifred is pursued
by Caradog

Saints Wordsearch

Abbey
George
Patrick
Scotland
England
Cuthbert
Saints
Margaret

Caedmon
David
Winifred
Snake
Poet
Bede
Faith
Augustine

Ireland
Chapel
Cathedral
Cross
Christian
Andrew
Hilda
Dunstan
Wales
Kentigern
Dragon
Knight
Monastery
Holy
Bravery
Legend
Festival
Monk
Religion
Jesus
Caradog
Mungo
Pope
Canterbury
Anglo Saxons
Danes
Malcolm
King
Myth
The Waterman
Dove
Leek
Salmon
Ring
Praying
Henry
Nun
Celtic
Devil
Shamrock
Asia
Greece
Blue
Red

```
A N D R E W T E K H J S P A T R I C K D C
V A U N M A B B E Y X C L P I O S D R F U
M I N D F L N B N A A S C O T L A N D M T
A B S L W E A A T D N D F L H K U E V N H
R H T A X S T H I L D A A S A I N T S M B
G P A A E Z R M G I X V N M E I W D T N E
A S N A G D A B E M F N F A I T H B N K R
R B F K L G E O R G E S D V H L J P O E T
E A C R U Y D G N W N O L R E W Q A F T B
T A A T B Q W A R Y G U A U G U S T I N E
T L E Y G W T P B H L Z S R L R D G R U I
D O D A V I D W E N A B L T C H A P E L Z
R Y M O N N U T D E N V H I A O J R L D F
A A O S G I W Q E R D N O I T I W M A K K
G L N D S F V Y P T S C L L H Y I D N F N
O K U A C R O S S W B B Y K E D B T D K I
N G I X M E E H H F Y I I G D R F H E T G
D H L P K D S J H N H I J L R A B F G F H
G M O N K O P C H R I S T I A N T E M H T
K Q F L U O L L J R W H D D L X R S J U Y
M O N A S T E R Y O J C P K H R W T L F J
L N A G P A S J Y E E O R E L I G I O N U
B R A V E R Y S C M S J J T U A D V E A Q
J G N D V R D D A N U P R T J C W A H L R
L D G G O Y V W R R S U A S I A J L H F I
E A L L D S K R A E O K R Y Y N N R H M N
G L O I N F I Y D A N E S P J T A S L A G
E J S S M U N G O H W L S R L E E K F S F
N Y A E A J G Y G E N U N X A R A G T Y K
D U X T L K L K W E Q L Y T U B L U E H S
H J O U C E K P R A Y I N G M U R T J J H
Y R N K O Y O L V Y E E R G I R P O C U A
R T S H L S I D Y J T H E N R Y R T E U M
K E H W M Y T H Y H F B K R U G G Y L D R
Y W G E L R I P E D R G W R Y J R P T S O
T H E W A T E R M A N F V P S D E O I Y C
J E K Y U Y P E W D O T Y O A Y E U C I K
H R J T I U W D T U P K L P H T C Y H F K
S A L M O N C U U S N A K E H D E V I L A
```

Funny Saints

There are many saints associated with all sorts of professions.
Here are just a few!

Restaurants
Martha

Bee Keepers
Ambrose, Bernard,
Modomnoc

Lighthousemen
Clement

Musicians
Cecilia, Gregory

Bricklayers
Stephen

Animals and birds
Francis of Assisi

Sailors
Nicholas, Francis of
Paola, Phocas

Firefighters
Agatha, Laurence

Bakers
Elizabeth of Hungry,
Zita

Travel
Christopher,
Julian, Magi

Thieves
Dismas

Television
Clare of Assisi

Florists
Dorothy, Rose of Lima

Horses
Giles, Hippolytus

Dentists
Apollonia

Astronauts
Joseph of Copertino

Search for a Saint

Look through your book and put the name of the saint next to
the picture they are associated with.

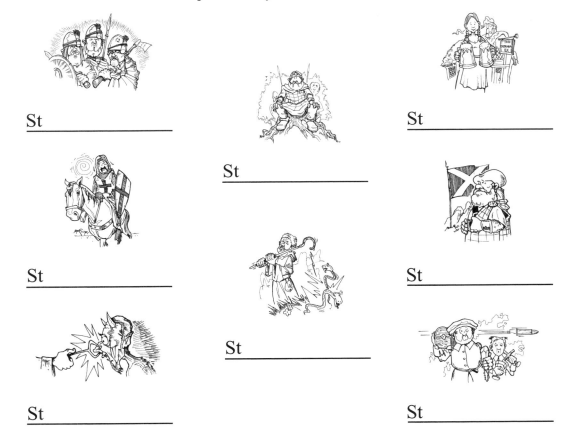

St _____

St _____

St _____

St _____

St _____

St _____

St _____

St _____

St _____

St Kentigern or Mungo c. 518 - 603 AD
Feast Day 13th January

Kentigern's mother came from a Celtic royal family. When she was discovered to be expecting a baby, the father of which was unknown, she was hurled over the edge of a steep cliff. She survived and was set adrift in a boat, landing at Culcross where a kind monk, St Serf, took pity on her and baby Kentigern. He called Kentigern "Mungo" meaning darling and taught him everything he knew.

As he grew older Kentigern felt the need to spend time alone and he moved to "Glashu", or Glasgow. He practised a strict life of prayer and soon a community gathered around him. He was appointed bishop, but these were troubled times and Kentigern was forced to flee to Wales, where he stayed with St David. He eventually returned to Scotland and died at age 85.

One myth tells of King Rydderch, who saw the ring he had given his queen, on the finger of one of his knights. While the knight slept, the king slipped the ring off his finger and threw it into the sea. He then asked his queen to produce the ring, or die if she could not. She turned to Kentigern for help and he ordered one of his monk's to fish in the sea. The monk caught a huge salmon, which had swallowed the ring and the queen's life was spared. The ring and the fish now form part of Glasgow's coat of arms.

St Augustine or Austin died c. 605 AD
Feast Day 26th May

Augustine was born in Italy and studied at the monastery of St Andrew in Rome. Pope St Gregory the Great was very impressed with Augustine and chose him to spread Christianity to the pagan Anglo-Saxons of England. Augustine and a band of more than 30 missionaries set off across Europe, but grew nervous as stories of the fierce Anglo-Saxons reached them. Greatly discouraged, Augustine returned to Rome.

As Pope St Gregory had received words of encouragement from England, Augustine was sent back. He landed in Kent in 597AD in Saxon King Ethelbert's territory and a meeting was arranged with the Christian missionaries. Augustine persuaded the king to allow him to stay and a base was established in Canterbury. Augustine travelled in the southern regions of England. By 601 AD Ethelbert and many of his noblemen were baptised. Pope St Gregory sent more clergy from Rome, and all of the necessary items for divine worship, such as alter cloths, sacred vessels, furniture and vestments.

St Gregory instructed that local customs and pagan temples should be kept and blessed for Christian worship. New schools were founded and Augustine helped Ethelbert to create the earliest Anglo-Saxon written laws. His death prevented him from spreading Christianity throughout the north of England, but he is recognised as one of England's most important Saints.

> *Did you know?*
> *King Ethelbert feared the magic spells Augustine could use against him, and decided to meet him in a woodland clearing as he believed the stranger's magic would not work outside!*

St Kentigern's monk catches
the huge salmon

St Hilda c. 614 - 680 AD
Feast Day 17th November

Hilda was related to royal families in Northumbria and East Anglia. She was baptised by St Paulinus when she was thirteen years old. A highly intelligent young woman she became abbess of Hartlepool. Later she was moved to Whitby, where she established the abbey as an important place of learning.

So good was her teaching that she trained at least five bishops and she encouraged people to read and write, and to take part in art and poetry. A stream of monks and scholars came to study under her guidance. Kings and leaders from all over the country came to her for help and advice. The poor, sick and uneducated were also able to ask Hilda for help. Her kindness, wisdom and generosity were legendary.

In 663AD a famous synod took place at Whitby Abbey, which reflected Hilda's importance. Many of the most influential religious leaders of that time were debating whether Britain should follow the Roman, or Celtic Christian teachings. It was agreed that they would follow the Roman way and gradually the Celtic teachings, which Hilda favoured, were lost. Hilda endured six years of very poor health before she died, but her enthusiasm, faith and gentle spirit remained until her last breath. Fifteen ancient English churches were dedicated to her memory. Whitby Abbey was almost completely destroyed by the Danes and Hilda's remains were supposedly taken to Glastonbury.

St Cuthbert c. 634 - 687 AD
Feast Day 20th March

Some of the most enchanting saintly stories surround St Cuthbert and the North East of England. He was the son of an Anglo-Saxon. Cuthbert enrolled as a monk, eventually becoming prior of Melrose Abbey and also Lindisfarne. He spent many hours praying, sometimes waist deep in the wild North Sea, and legend says that sea otters dried his legs and warmed his feet on returning to dry land. Ospreys would bring salmon to Cuthbert and man and bird would share the food together.

When Cuthbert died he was buried at Lindisfarne in 687. After the Vikings destroyed the monastery a group of monks took Cuthbert's remains, in his shrine, to find a place of safety to bury him. King Athelstan was said to have offered 96 lbs of silver, a book of his life and two gospel books to the shrine of Cuthbert. Reaching "Dunholm", or Durham they saw a dun cow sitting on the ground and took it as a sign of their journey's end.

A church was built on the site and St Cuthbert's remains were finally laid to rest. On the site today stands the magnificent Durham Cathedral. No less than 135 churches were dedicated to the memory of St Cuthbert.

> **Did you know?**
> *The Durham Ox is carved into the walls of Durham Cathedral and is a common pub name in the area.*

St Hilda encouraged education

St Caedmon died c. 680 AD
Feast Day 11th February

Caedmon came from humble beginnings and led a simple uneducated life. He was a large, rough looking man and worked for many years herding cows in the fields near Whitby Abbey. Every year at Christmas and Easter the workers on the Abbey estate would celebrate. During the festivities a harp would be passed around, and everyone would join in and sing popular songs together. Each time Caedmon would slip away quietly, returning to the barn where he slept, too embarrassed and shy to join in.

One night as Caedmon slept on the rough hay strewn floor, a voice spoke to him in the darkness. The voice asked him to sing and Caedmon suddenly found himself singing loudly, his head full of lyrics and poetry. The following morning Caedmon told the head man who took him to the Abbess Hilda. Impressed by his poetic verse, Hilda accepted him into the monastery where Caedmon turned Christian stories into beautiful, flowing poetry.

Caedmon was not a young man and after a short period of illness, he asked to be carried to the abbey infirmary. His friends told him that he looked well and promised he would soon recover, but as his head touched the pillow he peacefully passed away. Very little of his verse remains today, but Caedmon could be called the first English poet.

St Bede (The Venerable) c. 673 -735 AD
Feast Day 27th May

Bede was born near Sunderland in 673 and from the age of seven was educated by the church. He was ordained as a priest and was totally dedicated to learning, rarely travelling from his Jarrow monastery. He had no influence with kings, or life outside the monastery, but it is fair to say that he was the most educated man of his time. Bede has become famous for his writing on mathematics, poetry, the life and times of other saints, timekeeping and updating ancient scriptures. His books are an important part of modern day understanding of ancient history in early Britain.

In 735 Bede became ill as he worked on a translation of the ancient gospel of St John. Retiring to his room he continued to dictate his work to the young boy working as his scribe. Bede called for the priests to sit by his bedside and opening a box gave them pepper, incense and linen. Then, after dictating a final chapter, he sang a prayer and peacefully died.

St Bede's relics were said to make miraculous cures. His bones were removed from Jarrow and were eventually taken to Durham Cathedral. A number of schools have been dedicated to his memory, reflecting his inspiration to scholars.

Did you know?
Whitby Abbey has been badly damaged three times, first the Danes, then Henry VIII's soldiers and in World War I by German naval gunfire!

Caedmon was awakened by a voice in the darkness

St Dunstan c. 909 - 988 AD
Feast Day 19th May

St Dunstan was born with royal connections and was educated at Glastonbury Abbey. He joined his uncle, the Archbishop of Canterbury and then the court of King Athelstan. He became a great favourite with the king, but members of the court were jealous and he was wrongly accused of studying pagan stories and magic. He was dismissed from the king's service and flung into a filthy pit.

In his thirties he found it difficult to commit himself fully to life in the church, and began to suffer from a terrible skin disease. Dunstan feared he had caught leprosy and took this as a sign that he must begin a new life. Fully recovered he returned to Glastonbury Abbey, spending long days in a workshop, producing beautiful church bells and vessels. The new king, Edmund, was very impressed and appointed Dunstan abbot of Glastonbury in 943 AD. Dunstan transformed the abbey buildings and it became a great school.

King Edmund was murdered and his brother Edred succeeded him, making Dunstan his chief adviser. Dunstan's policies made him unpopular and when Edred died his 16 year old nephew became king. Following a disagreement Dunstan was expelled to Europe, but soon a rebellion took place in Britain and Edgar became king. Immediately Dunstan was called back and eventually become Archbishop of Canterbury. He is credited with forging closer links between the monarchy and the church, some of which still exist today.

St Margaret c. 1046 - 1093 AD
Feast Day 16th November

Margaret was one of the last members of the Anglo-Saxon royal family, and in great danger after the Norman Conquest. Her early years were spent in exile in Hungary, as England was ruled by the Danes. When she returned to Britain she sought refuge at the court of King Malcolm III of Scotland.

Malcolm was rough and uncultured, and he admired the beautiful and intelligent Margaret. Eventually she agreed to marry him and the marriage was a great success. They established several churches, Dunfermline being the most famous one. Over the next 23 years Malcolm and Margaret had eight children and ruled Scotland together. Abbeys were established, schools built and the queen visited and gave money to the poor and sick. King Malcolm and the court were introduced to fashion and good manners from Europe and trade and prosperity came to Scotland.

King Malcolm was devoted to his wife and although he was unable to read and write, he encouraged and admired her work. The uneasy peace with the English was shattered when William Rufus became the new king. Malcolm led his Scottish army into England, where he and his eldest son were killed in battle. The heartbroken Queen died 4 days later and they were buried together in Dunfermline Abbey.

Did you know?
Legend tells us that the devil appeared before Dunstan in order to tempt him. Using the red hot pincers he was working with, Dunstan lunged at the devil, catching him by the nose and overpowered him.

St Dunstan was flung
into a filthy pit

Saintly Quiz

1. When is St Dunstan's feast day?

2. Which vegetable were the ancient Briton's asked to wear in their caps?

3. Who cut off St Winifred's head?

4. Where was St Patrick born?

5. Which Saint established Whitby Abbey?

6. Which Saint could claim to be England's first English poet?

7. Who is the patron Saint of England?

8. Where did St Rule become shipwrecked?

9. St Bede took three things from a box, what were they?

10. Which Saint was the first missionary in Asia and Greece?

11. What did St Patrick supposedly banish from Ireland with his magic staff?

12. What is the name of the original patron Saint of Wales?

13. What does "Mungo" mean?

14. Why did King Ethelbert of Kent decide to meet with Augustine outside?

15. How many children did St Margaret and King Malcolm have?

16. What does the cross on the flag of Scotland represent?

17. What is the most famous legend of St George?

18. What does the symbol of a clover leaf, or shamrock represent?

19. What did St Serf call Kentigern?

20. In 444 AD what did St Patrick found?

21. What now stands where St Cuthbert's remains were finally laid to rest?

22. Can you name three of the topics which St Bede wrote about?

23. In which World War was Whitby Abbey damaged by naval gunfire?

24. What was St David's nickname?

Answers 1. 19th May. 2. A leek. 3. Caradog. 4. England. 5. St Hilda. 6. St Caedmon. 7. St George. 8. East Coast of Scotland. 9. Pepper, incense and linen. 10. St Andrew. 11. Snakes. 12. St Winifred. 13. Darling. 14. The King believed the stranger's magic would not work outside. 15. 8. 16. The crucifix on which St Andrew died. 17. The slaying of the dragon. 18. St Patrick described the 3 leaves as representing the father, the son and the Holy Spirit. 19. Mungo. 20. Cathedral church of Armagh. 21. Durham Cathedral. 22. Mathematics, poetry, the life and times of other saints, timekeeping and updating ancient scriptures. 23. World War 1. 24. The Waterman